Roderick Hunt

Comprehension plus

BOOK 4

Contents

Oxford University Press

A stranger's nightmare

Air Marshal Sir Victor Goddard of the New Zealand Air Force once met a man who was startled to see him alive and well. 'Your plane crashed last night after the wings iced up,' stammered the man. 'You had been flying over mountains. There was a terrible snowstorm. The plane came down on a rocky shore in Japan. I . . . I saw it happen.'

The man's face turned red and he apologized. 'I'm so sorry,' he said. 'You see I had a dream last night. It was so vivid I thought it must be true. You were in a Dakota with an RAF crew and three passengers—two men and a woman.'

The Air Marshal smiled. 'Well, I am, in fact, flying to Tokyo *tomorrow* in a Dakota. But there are no passengers so I don't think your dream will come true.'

Later the next day, however, three people asked if they could join the flight as passengers. They were two men and a woman—just as the stranger had foreseen.

Just before take-off the Air Marshal had a strange feeling of dread. The weather forecast showed that there was bad weather ahead. It was very cold. There was snow about. Could the stranger's dream be coming true?

On the flight the pilot reported heavy ice on the wings. The plane began to lose height. As the ice thickened it was forced into a crash landing. Through the driving snow could be seen a rocky coast. The only place to land was on the shore. Thanks to the skill of the pilot the plane crash-landed without anyone being hurt. But things had come true just as the stranger had seen them in his dream.

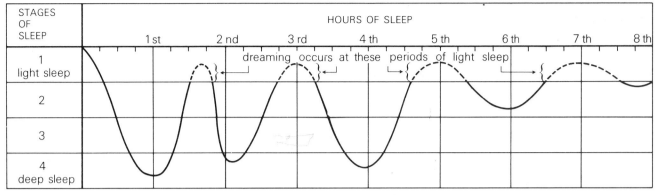

STAGES OF SLEEP	HOURS OF SLEEP							
	1st	2nd	3rd	4th	5th	6th	7th	8th
1 light sleep								
2								
3								
4 deep sleep								

dreaming occurs at these periods of light sleep

Did you dream last night? Everyone dreams at night, not once but four or five times. Dreams occur in a regular pattern so that during an eight-hour period of sleep we dream about every ninety minutes. And the length of each dream gets longer as the night goes on. Scientists have recorded the depth of sleep by measuring brain waves. They have found that first we sink into a deep sleep. Then our levels of sleep rise and fall. As we dream our eyes flicker rapidly under our eyelids as if we are following the dream with our eyes. If you think you didn't dream last night it is because you have forgotten what you dreamt.

A Write sentences to answer these questions.

1 Why was the stranger startled to see the Air Marshal?
2 Why was the man embarrassed?
3 What did the man say had caused the plane to crash?
4 Where did he say the plane had come down?
5 What kind of plane did the man see in his dream?
6 What, in fact, was the Air Marshal intending to do the next day?
7 In what way did the man's dream then begin to come true?
8 Why did the Air Marshal have a feeling of dread?
9 Why did the plane lose height on the flight?
10 What happened, thanks to the pilot?

B Here are some words which begin with *fore-*

forecast (noun)—an estimate of coming weather
foresee (verb)—to see or know beforehand
foreboding (noun)—a feeling of approaching disaster
forewarn (verb)—to warn someone beforehand

Put these four words in the right gaps in the following:
We could not _____ that the weather _____ would be so full of _____, or we would have been able to _____ them that a storm was due.

C Use the information at the top of this page to answer the following questions.

1 How often do dreams occur during a normal night's sleep?
2 When do the longest dreams take place?
3 How do scientists record our sleep patterns?
4 What happens to our eyes as we dream?

D Discuss dreams using the following points to help you.

1 Do you generally remember your dreams?
2 Have you ever had a dream come true?
3 Have you ever had a vivid dream which you can still remember?
4 What is a nightmare? Do you ever have nightmares?

E Some ideas for writing.

1 Have you ever had a vivid dream? If you can still remember it, write down what it was about.
2 Write a story about a dream that comes true. It could either be a warning, or a dream that has a happy outcome.
3 Write a story about an invention called 'Dial-a-dream', which you plug yourself into before you go to sleep.

Sixth sense

During the very hot summer of 1975 in the USA, Mrs Stevenson of Wheatley, Arkansas, had to go shopping, but her son Bobby, ten years old, wanted to go swimming in a nearby pool. The pool was a safe place to swim. Most of Bobby's friends would be there.

The shopping centre was only half a mile (0.8 km.) from the pool. Mrs Stevenson dropped Bobby off and drove on. But in the store, she was gripped by a feeling of terror. She could hardly breathe. She felt as though she was choking. Then she realized that it was her son Bobby who couldn't breathe. Bobby was choking. He was drowning!

Mrs Stevenson ran to her car.
'I broke the speed laws and drove through a red light to get there!' she said later.
She did not see Bobby in the water. The other children said they had not seen him for some time.
'I ran to the deep end,' she said. 'He was lying on the bottom. Two of the older boys dived in and brought him out. He wasn't breathing.'

It took several minutes to revive the boy. But Bobby Stevenson lived to tell the story.

What happened to Mrs Stevenson when she was shopping? Why did she panic and feel she was choking at the very moment that Bobby was in trouble under the water? Was it just a chance—a coincidence? Or is there more to it than that?

Types of ESP

A man dreams of someone he has never seen in his life; the next day he meets the stranger, just as he saw him in his dream. A woman goes to a strange house, but has the feeling she has been there before. Two people have exactly the same thought at the same time. One person is sent a message from another, through their minds.

All these are examples of something that happens in people's minds that cannot be explained. It is known as *sixth sense*, or ESP (extra-sensory perception).

Precognition—knowing something is going to happen before it does.

Telepathy—knowing what someone else is thinking.

Clairvoyance—knowing something without having any way of finding out about it.

A **Write sentences to answer the following questions.**

1 Why was Mrs Stevenson not worried about Bobby going off to swim in the pool?
2 Why is it likely that Bobby had been to the pool many times before during that summer?
3 What sensation did Mrs Stevenson experience while she was shopping in the store?
4 What did she think was happening to Bobby?
5 What did Mrs Stevenson do?
6 What do you think *might* have happened if Mrs Stevenson had a friend or her husband with her at the time?
7 How do *you* think Mrs Stevenson realized that her son was in trouble?

B The prefix *tele-* comes from a Greek word (tele) meaning *far* or *distant*. These pictures represent four words all beginning with tele-. Write the words down and choose *one* to explain how the meaning *far* or *distant* can be applied to it.

C **Look at the information about ESP at the top of this page and answer the following questions.**

1 What do the letters ESP stand for?
2 What *is* ESP?
3 What type of ESP is it when a man dreams about a stranger and meets the stranger the next day?

4 What type of ESP is it when a woman feels she knows a house she has never been to?

D **Discuss ESP using the following points to help you.**

What is a *coincidence?*

1 Discuss the story of Mrs Stevenson and her son Bobby. Do you think it was a case of telepathy or was it just a coincidence?
2 Have you ever had exactly the same thought at the same time as someone else? Was it telepathy?
3 Have you ever had the feeling you know all about a place you have never been to?
4 Try this experiment, either with a friend, or with a group. One person has to read the mind of another (or others) who are thinking of ONE of the following shapes:

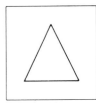

E **Some ideas for writing.**

1 Write a story about an animal that refuses to go somewhere and won't let you go there either. Later you find out that the animal saved you from danger.
2 Write a story which ends, 'Well, I've been trying to tell you all along that we should never have come here.'
3 Write a story that ends, 'I had a feeling it was going to happen.'
4 Write a story about someone who receives a message by telepathy from someone they've never met, or from a famous historical character.

Safety on the road

	PEDESTRIANS			PEDAL CYCLISTS		
killed	113	216	134	3	20	75
seriously injured	1,003	3,591	2,868	16	504	1,257
slightly injured	2,880	9,822	8,282	91	1,556	5,215
AGE GROUP	0 – 4 years	5 – 9 years	10 – 14 years	0 – 4 years	5 – 9 years	10 – 14 years

This chart shows the number of children involved in road accidents during one year.

A Look at the picture on the opposite page. Make a list of all the possible causes of accidents in the road. Who do you think is in the greatest danger in the picture?

B Copy out the following sentences putting the right words in the gaps.

junction   casualty   pedestrian   vehicle   cyclist

1 A _____ is a person who uses the highway on foot.
2 A _____ is a person who is on a bicycle.
3 A _____ is a person who has met with an accident.
4 A _____ is the point where roads meet.
5 A _____ is a car, van, lorry or motorbike.

C Look at the chart of figures about accidents involving children and answer these questions.

1 Compare the total number of accidents in the pedestrian section with the total number in the cyclist section. Of the two, which has the greater total?
2 Which age group has the greatest number of fatal accidents (children killed) out of pedestrians or cyclists?
3 Which age group among the pedestrians has the most accidents overall?
4 Which age group among the cyclists has the most accidents overall?
5 Why do you think the age group 5–9 has the most accidents among the pedestrians?
6 Why do you think the age group 10–14 has the most accidents among the cyclists?
7 Why do you think there are fewer accidents among the 0–4 age group?

D Discuss road safety using the following points to help you.

1 What is The Highway Code? Why should every road user know what's in it?
2 What is the law relating to the safety of your bicycle?
3 What is the difference between a Pelican Crossing and a Zebra Crossing?
4 What is the Green Cross Code? What does it say?
5 Think of four places where cyclists are forbidden to ride. Are there any more?

E Some ideas for writing.

Write a story about *one* of the following characters who didn't bother about road safety, and ended up learning a lesson.

Daredevil Diane   Shortsighted Sue

Reckless Roderick   Mr and Mrs Blunder

F What do the following roadsigns mean?

(shaded area—red)

The priest's hole

At Christmas in 1599 the Jesuit priest, Father Blount, was staying at Scotney Castle in Kent. The castle belonged to the Darrell family who were Catholics. At that time it was against the law to have a Catholic priest in the house.

Suddenly, just after midnight, there was uproar. The castle was being raided by priest-hunting soldiers.

Before the soldiers had time to search the castle, Father Blount and his servant rushed to a secret hiding-place in the outside wall of the castle courtyard. This was a tiny space called a priest's hole. It was hidden in the wall behind a large stone which swung open on hinges.

As the priest and his servant scrambled into the priest's hole, the cord of Father Blount's robe caught in the stone door. It was left hanging out of the wall for all to see.

The soldiers shut Mrs Darrell in a room. Mr Darrell was away. For a week they searched the castle. They pulled up floor-boards, tore down ceilings and ripped off wall-panels. They did not notice the tell-tale cord hanging on the wall.

Meanwhile, the two men in hiding were having a bad time. All they had on was their night-clothes and it was bitterly cold. They were also very hungry.

At last Mrs Darrell was set free. As soon as she thought it was safe, she went to the hiding-place. She was shocked to find the cord hanging out of the wall. 'Pull the cord in,' she called quietly. This Father Blount did.

However, Mrs Darrell was being watched by two of the searchers. Seeing her pause by the courtyard wall they became suspicious. They fetched a hammer and began to break down the wall, hoping to discover the priest's hole.

Luckily it began to rain heavily so the searchers gave up for the night. Taking a chance Father Blount and his servant came out of the priest's hole and managed to escape by swimming across the freezing moat.

Even today, visitors to Scotney gaze closely at its ancient walls. The hinged stone and the hiding-place behind it have never been discovered.

Some of history's most cunning hiding-places were built in England between 1558 and 1603 after Queen Elizabeth I had outlawed all Catholic priests and forbidden Catholics to practise their religion. Any priest who was caught was liable to be executed.

Despite these laws, specially trained priests were smuggled back to England to hold secret services in private homes.

These homes were often raided by priest-hunters so hiding-places called 'priest's holes' were built. These were tiny spaces cunningly concealed under floors or stairs, behind false walls or even in chimneys.

So cleverly concealed were these hides that the priest-hunters might spend days searching in a house and still fail to discover them.

A Write sentences to answer these questions.

1 Whom had the priest-hunters gone to Scotney Castle to arrest?
2 Where was the hiding-place situated?
3 Why was the hiding-place so difficult to spot?
4 What happened as Father Blount scrambled into the priest's hole which could have revealed where he was hiding?
5 How long were the two men in hiding?
6 How did Mrs Darrell arouse the suspicion of the priest-hunters?
7 How did the priest and his servant finally manage to escape from the castle?
8 Has the whereabouts of the secret hiding-place ever been discovered?

B Write out the following sentences putting the correct word from the list in each gap.

discovered   revealed   concealed   pursued
disguised   smuggled   raided

1 The priest-hunters never _____ the secret hiding-place in the castle wall.
2 The hidden room was cleverly _____ behind a secret door in the wall.
3 The secret door swung open and _____ a hidden room.
4 The escaper was _____ across the frontier by the border guards.
5 The escaper was _____ into the country in the back of a lorry.
6 The escaper crossed the border _____ as a woman.
7 The castle was _____ by priest-hunting soldiers.

C Copy out this paragraph putting the correct words in the gaps. Use the information at the top of this page to help you.

Despite the laws which Queen _____ passed forbidding _____ to practise their _____, many _____ were smuggled into England between _____ and _____. Secret _____ were held in _____ homes, but there was always a danger of raids by _____ _____. So cunningly concealed hiding-places called _____ _____ were built.

D Discuss priest's holes and hiding-places. Then discuss the following.

1 Do you have a special hiding-place, hideout, hidey-hole or secret den? Imagine you could have the perfect hideout. What would it be like?
2 Some boys once got shut in an old deep-freeze on a rubbish dump. It was a terrible experience. What is the difference between hiding and being shut in?

E Some ideas for writing.

1 Imagine you have to construct a secret hiding-place (like a priest's hole) either in your own home, or somewhere you know very well. How would you do it? What would it be like? How would you make sure that no one could find you once you were inside?

2 Write a story about the discovery of a priest's hole or a secret room in an old house you visit with a friend. What is in the secret room? Maybe it contains something valuable, or even something terrible.

3 Write a story about hiding.

Heraldry

In battle a knight in full armour needed to be recognized easily. So he wore a distinctive coat over his armour. This was called a *coat of arms*. At first these coats had very simple designs so that they were clearly visible even at a distance. The design was displayed on the knight's banner, his horse and, most important of all, on his shield.

As time went on, a knight's coat of arms came to be used away from the battlefield as his personal symbol. It showed he was a man of rank and importance. These personal symbols were very elaborate. They are known as *achievements of arms*.

Helmet Crest Wreath Mantle Shield Scroll Motto

EXALTABIT · HONORE

The main feature of an achievement of arms for a knight was the *shield* but it included his *helmet* with the special *crest* he wore on the helmet top. It showed the *wreath* which was wound round the bottom of the crest and also the cloth, or *mantle* which hung from the helmet to protect the knight from the hot sun. It also had a *scroll* with a *motto*.

The shield. The surface or background of a shield is called the *field*. Some of the very first coats of arms had plain shields all of one colour but usually a pattern or device was placed on them. At first these devices were either simple geometric shapes or lines dividing the shield into areas of contrasting colours:

Only five colours are used in heraldry. These are red, blue, black, green, and purple. In addition there are gold and silver, but these are regarded as metals, not colours. Animal furs are also used as a background, the most common being *ermine* (white and black stoat fur) and *vair* (blue and white squirrel fur):

There are many complicated rules to do with coats of arms. Heralds are people who make sure these rules are carried out.

A man's children are not allowed to have exactly the same coat of arms as their father. They have to make a small change to the coat. One way this is done is to give each son a special mark in order of birth. After a man's death his coat of arms passes to his eldest son.

After a marriage the wife's coat of arms is placed beside her husband's on his shield. In some cases the children may divide the shield into quarters. If several generations of children marry persons entitled to bear arms, the shield is *quartered* many times.

A Write sentences to answer these questions.

1 Why do you think a knight in full armour needed to be recognized easily.
2 What did a knight wear to make sure that he was recognized?
3 Where did a knight display his own distinctive design?
4 What happened to the coats of arms as time went on?
5 What is the name given to these personal symbols?
6 Make a list of all the features that make up an achievement of arms?
7 Why do you think the shield is the most important feature?
8 Why did a knight wear a mantle?
9 What is the writing on the scroll of an achievement of arms called?
10 Whose job is it to make sure that all the rules to do with coats of arms are carried out?

B Add one of these endings:

-ise, -hood, -ment, -ive, -al, -ry
to the following list of words to form new words
e.g. *-ry* + *herald* = heraldry

distinct   symbol
knight   achieve

Now try these:

man   rival
advert   content

C Use the information on heraldry at the top of this page to answer these questions.

1 What must a man's children do to their coats of arms?
2 Whom does the coat of arms pass to?
3 What happens to a woman's coat of arms after her marriage?
4 When is a coat of arms *quartered*?

D This is the personal shield of eleven year-old Martin Locke. Martin designed the shield for a competition. In each quarter he has put little emblems about himself.

You can see from the shield where Martin comes in his family, what his hobbies and interests are, and even which soccer team he supports.

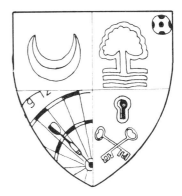

Design your own personal shield. Maybe you could include little emblems which tell all about you in each quarter.

Who was in the right?

In these pictures you can see an incident between a cyclist and a motorist in a shopping street.
Who was to blame?
Was it the driver of the car, the boy on the bicycle or the dog that ran across the road?

A Driver's statement
'I was driving up the High Street towards the traffic lights. Suddenly a dog ran out into the road. I pulled over slightly to avoid the dog. At the same time the cyclist swerved out suddenly right in my path. He rode straight under my front wheel. It really wasn't my fault. I'm a salesman and I have to travel hundreds of miles a week. I can't afford to get involved in accidents like this.'

B Boy's statement

'I was cycling quite normally up the High Street. There was a drain on the edge of the road and it threw my front wheel off course a little. The car was obviously too close to me. I don't think the driver was looking where he was going. The street's wide enough for him to get past! I reckon he wants his eyes testing!'

C Woman's statement

'The trouble with drivers these days is they're too impatient. They go much too fast up this road. Sometimes I take my life in my hands when I want to cross. They go speeding . . .'
(Policeman asks her to say only what she saw)

'Yes, well, I heard this car come racing up the street. He can't have been looking where he was going. I expect he was breaking the speed limit. He didn't give the cyclist a chance. Such a screech of brakes! It really made me jump.'

A 1 In what way was the driver not paying attention just before the accident?

2 From what the driver said, what did he not notice about the way the boy was cycling?

3 What actions should the driver have taken if he had seen the dog and noticed the way the boy was cycling?

4 How did the driver try to blame the cyclist?

B 1 Why is it likely that the boy *did* swerve out into the road?

2 How did the boy try to blame the driver?

C 1 From what the woman said, do you think she is a reliable witness?

2 Which sentence shows that she did not really see the accident?

3 What reason does the woman have for deciding to blame the driver even though she did not see what happened?

D Draw the crossword grid below and complete it using the clues given.

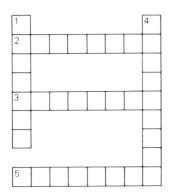

1 Someone who has seen an event, and who is asked to say what happened.

2 Something unexpected that happens, often without warning.

3 Information given, or facts collected together to show what happened.

4 A person's account of what they think happened which is written down.

5 A mishap; an event that was not expected to happen, and having a sad or unwanted outcome.

E Discuss being a witness using the following points to help you.

1 Were the driver and the boy telling lies, or were they simply not telling the whole truth? Discuss why people often don't tell the whole truth?

2 What does being observant mean? Why can it be difficult to describe someone or to describe an incident that you have witnessed?

3

I
LOVE
PARIS IN THE
THE SPRING

Read the words in this triangle. How does the problem here help to explain how the woman was thinking? What does 'jumping to conclusions' mean?

F Some ideas for writing.

1 Look at picture 2. What other evidence would the policeman be able to give when he made his report?

2 Imagine you had seen the accident clearly. Write a short statement saying what happened, and how much you think the driver and the cyclist were to blame.

It's a noisy world

We live in a world full of sounds. In the busy street we're quite used to the sound of traffic—the thrum of a motor-bike, for example, or the blaring of a car horn; the rumble of a bus or the hiss of a lorry's air-brakes.

We are quite accustomed to the sound of a jet plane roaring overhead, a train clattering by, or a tractor rattling away in the distance.

In our homes there are many sounds which we wouldn't like to be without—the sound of the television, the radio or the record player. And how about all those familiar, homely sounds like the clink of cups, the swish of water or the whistle of a kettle?

Any of these sounds is bearable on its own. Yet if any one of them is too loud, or if several sounds are heard all at the same time, the result is—*noise*.

To most people, noise depends on how a sound is heard. Someone trying to sleep may be irritated by the ticking of a clock. A person using a saw may not be bothered by the noise of it, but someone trying to read certainly is.

In fact, some sorts of noise can be harmful or even dangerous. People who work in very noisy factories without protection for their ears become deaf, many of them seriously

In the USA scientists made tests on the hearing of young people who went regularly to very noisy pop music concerts and discos. Many of the young people were found to have permanent ear damage. Several suffered serious deafness.

When your teacher tells you to work quietly, or in silence, there's a good reason. Scientists say that people trying to concentrate in noisy surroundings can waste as much as 25 per cent of their energy simply because of the noise.

The intensity of sounds is measured in units called decibels.

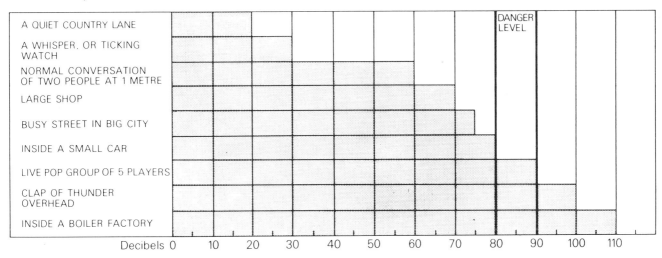

	Decibels 0	10	20	30	40	50	60	70	80 DANGER LEVEL	90	100	110

A QUIET COUNTRY LANE
A WHISPER, OR TICKING WATCH
NORMAL CONVERSATION OF TWO PEOPLE AT 1 METRE
LARGE SHOP
BUSY STREET IN BIG CITY
INSIDE A SMALL CAR
LIVE POP GROUP OF 5 PLAYERS
CLAP OF THUNDER OVERHEAD
INSIDE A BOILER FACTORY

A Write sentences to answer these questions.

1 Which vehicles does the writer of the article mention in the first paragraph?
2 The writer gives examples of familiar sounds in the home e.g. *the swish of water*. Write down an example of your own.
3 In what two ways does the writer suggest that noise is produced?
4 When might the ticking of a clock be thought of as noise?
5 What precautions should people take when working in noisy surroundings?
6 What effect can too much loud noise have on a person's hearing?
7 How much energy can be wasted trying to concentrate against noise?

B Match each word in the first column with one of a similar meaning in the second column.

accustomed	lasting
irritated	used to
dangerous	annoyed
permanent	injurious

C Discuss the chart at the top of this page.

1 How is the loudness of sound measured?
2 Above how many decibels is noise considered harmful or dangerous?
3 From the examples given on the chart, how many decibels do you think might be recorded:
  a during an activity lesson in your classroom?
  b during hymn singing in assembly?
  c in an indoor swimming-pool?
  d when your teacher shouts at you?

4 Think of some everyday sounds that might register more than 80–90 decibels (e.g. a pneumatic drill).

D In the first twelve lines of the article on noise, the writer uses nine sound words e.g. *thrum* (line 2) *swish* (line 12). Make a list of the nine sound words.

Make a list of sound words which could be used to describe what it's like at the seaside e.g. the *crash* of waves, the *scream* of seagulls

Make a list of sound words for some of these:

  the zoo   the fairground   the supermarket

The following words all make the sound they are supposed to describe:

  click pop boom thud crunch

Give one or more sound words like these for each of the following:

  snake   clock   hammer   water   bell   dog

E Some ideas for writing.

1 You are alone in a street at night. Perhaps it is your street. You listen to all the sounds around you. Some are very close, some are far away. Think of as many sounds as you can, then write a story or poem called 'A street at night'.
2 Imagine a tiger roaring like a motor horn or a mouse sounding like a vacuum cleaner. Write a funny story about the day that sounds changed places.
3 Write a poem describing or using all sorts of sound or sound words.

A theatre on the table

Before there was television to watch or radio to listen to, families had to entertain themselves in the evenings. During the nineteenth century one popular form of family entertainment was the toy theatre.

A toy theatre is a tiny model stage with a colourful arch over it. Such theatres are usually made of card. They have paper scenery which can be changed for different scenes of a play. The 'actors' are little cut-out figures. They are fixed to long wires and are pushed on to the stage from the side. At the end of each scene a set of paper curtains is let down in front of the stage.

The idea of toy theatres was developed by a man called William West. In 1811 he published sheets of card printed with sets of cut-out figures from a popular play or story.

West also produced sheets of scenery. Some of these were exact copies of stage settings in famous London theatres. People who would never be able to go to a London theatre themselves could imagine what it was like by having a little cardboard model of one in their own homes.

During the long dark evenings when the curtains were drawn and a coal fire blazed in the hearth, the family would set up their model and pretend they were at the theatre.

The demand for West's plays grew and grew. During his lifetime he produced over 140 different plays. Soon the idea of toy theatres spread to other countries.

In Germany the sheets of characters and scenery were very elaborate. Often they were three or four times bigger than those produced in Britain. The best-loved plays were *Hansel and Gretel* and *William Tell*.

You can easily make a toy theatre and produce your own play. Trace the figures at the top of this page (or draw some of your own) on to thin card and colour them in. Bend the flaps under and glue each figure to a long thin strip of card. Make your theatre from a cardboard box (a cornflake packet would do). Make a colourful theatre arch and glue it to the front. Write your play to suit the characters you have cut out, or write your play first and then make your characters to play the parts. It is best to start with only two (or perhaps three) characters and write just a short scene for them to act.

A Write sentences to answer these questions.

1 What was one popular family entertainment during the early nineteenth century?
2 What is a toy theatre?
3 What are toy theatres usually made of?
4 How are the figures in a toy theatre made and how do they come on to the stage?
5 Who developed the idea of toy theatres?
6 What did William West copy?
7 What were people able to pretend when they had a toy theatre?
8 How many different plays did William West produce?
9 What were the play-sheets like in Germany?

B Here are some words from the article on toy theatres that are tricky to spell. Copy out the sentences putting the correct word in each gap.

scenery   characters   curtain   colour   theatre
elaborate   different

1 You may like to set up a toy _____.
2 It need not be very _____.
3 Draw your _____ on to thin card and _____ them in with felt tips or crayons.
4 You could also design some _____ and change it when you have a _____ scene.
5 Don't forget to bring down the _____ at the end.

C Take a long word from the passage on toy theatres and write it in the centre of a piece of paper. Then find as many words as you can *from the passage* and build them on to your long word. Here is an example using the word ENTERTAINMENT

```
                            P
                       F    L
B                      I D E A
I                      G    Y
G    A                 U
G    C                 R
E N T E R T A I N M E N T
R    O    H
     R    E
          A    A
        S T O R Y
          R    C
          E    H
```

D Here are some ideas for short plays for your toy theatre. Try writing a scene for some of them.

1 The first men on the moon step out of their landing craft and look around—but on the moon's surface they discover a cigarette packet.
2 Some friends go to a haunted house and discover a ghost—in tears!
3 Two children are walking in a forest and come across a witch with a broken broomstick.
4 A mad scientist's experiment goes wrong. A spider begins to grow, and it gets bigger and bigger . . .
5 A dentist's first patient is Count Dracula—with toothache. This time it's the dentist who is nervous.

Robots

What comes into your mind when you think about robots? Do you imagine armies of evil metal monsters planning to take over the world? Or, perhaps of mechanical men who have been created as guards or soldiers by a mad genius? Or maybe you think of man-like robots (called androids) who act, think, and look like human beings.

In fact robots like these have more to do with science fiction films than with real life. In the real world robots are machines that do jobs which otherwise have to be done by people. Robots either operate by themselves (automatically), or under the control of a person.

In a car factory, for example, robot machinery can weld together and paint-spray car bodies. On the sea bed remote controlled underwater machines (submersibles) with mechanical arms can perform tasks too difficult for divers. Robot spacecraft can explore the solar system and send back information (data) about planets and asteroids.

Many robots have computer brains which deal with (process) information fed into them. Some robots are fitted with cameras, sensors, and microphones which enable them to see, to feel, and to hear. And some robots have a device called a voice synthesizer which produces electronic speech.

All this does not mean that a robot can think and behave like a human being. Present day robots have to be programmed with a good deal of information before they can carry out even simple tasks.

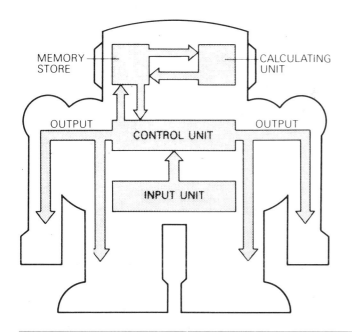

MEMORY STORE

CALCULATING UNIT

OUTPUT

CONTROL UNIT

OUTPUT

INPUT UNIT

A robot brain

The 'brain' of a robot is a computer. The robot is taught by programming the computer. The program is a set of instructions that tell the computer what to do with the information it receives from the robot's 'eyes', 'ears', or other sensors.

The program and other information are fed into the input unit and stored in the memory.

The instructions are carried out by the calculating unit.

The control unit controls the whole computer, and it also directs the output signals to the various parts of the robot.

A Write sentences to answer these questions.

1 What kind of robot is an *android*?
2 What is meant by *science fiction*? What sort of films and stories are science fiction?
3 What *are* robots?
4 What kinds of jobs do robots do in car factories?
5 Where can robots be sent where humans would find it difficult or impossible to go?
6 Apart from their computer 'brains', with what other devices can robots be equipped?
7 What must be done to a robot before it can carry out a simple task?

B Write down the meaning of each of the following words:

e.g. android—a manlike robot, which thinks and acts like a human being.

automatically   data
remote control   process
submersible

C Write sentences to answer these questions about the information on this page.

1 What is a robot 'brain' called?
2 How is the robot 'taught'?
3 What is a program?
4 Into which unit is the program 'fed'?
5 Where is the information stored?
6 Which unit carries out the instructions?
7 What does the control unit do?

D Discuss robots using the following points to help you.

1 Discuss robot devices in aeroplanes.
2 Supposing every home could have a robot. What sort of jobs do you think it would be able to do?
3 Supposing every school could have a robot. Would it be a good idea to have robot teachers?
4 How would robots be useful in hospitals? Would it be possible to have robot nurses?
5 If robots take over jobs that people have always done, what do you think this means will happen to the way people work?

E Some ideas for writing.

1 Write about your favourite film or T.V. robot.
2 Write an account of how you think man could develop robots to help mankind.

Touchdown on the red planet

The sky above the planet is cloudless and empty. There are no aeroplanes and no birds. There is nothing, only a strange pink light changing to blue as the sun sets.

The surface of the planet is bleak and rocky. No living thing moves. Nothing stirs, only a dry wind blowing dust storms across the parched red deserts.

High above the planet is a single spacecraft. It is at the end of a 500-million-mile journey. It has circled the planet twice, moving silently above the desolate landscape. Below the spacecraft there lie huge dead volcanoes, deep rocky canyons and vast winding channels that look like dried-up river beds.

Suddenly a landing-craft detaches itself from the spacecraft and begins a one-way journey to a chosen landing place near the planet's equator.

Travelling at 8,400 miles an hour, the landing craft enters the planet's atmosphere. The underside of the tiny craft glows white-hot as it slows to the speed of sound.

A parachute snaps open, halting the land-craft's crazy speed. Next the bottom part of the falling craft separates and floats free. It drops down over a 15-mile-high volcano. It passes the 23,000-metre peaks of a giant mountain range. Now it is dead on course for its landing place in a wide flat valley.

Finally its three braking rockets fire. Its landing legs snap out and lock into position. Plumes of ice-blue flame from the braking rockets grow longer. The tiny craft hovers above the ground. One leg touches down, then another. The rockets cut out and the landing craft settles on the untrodden surface with a gentle, creaking groan.

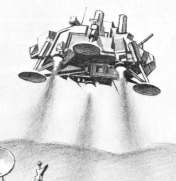

In 1976, two amazing robots, Viking 1 and Viking 2, landed on the surface of Mars to send back vital information about the planet to scientists on Earth.

The robots took photographs of the Martian landscape. They recorded movements of the ground and tested soil and rock samples. The robots did not see any Martians. The air on Mars is mostly carbon dioxide gas. Scientists say that with air temperatures way below anything ever recorded on Earth and with deadly radiation from the sun striking the ground, it is unlikely that Mars can support any kind of life.

A Write sentences to answer these questions.

1 What is the surface of the planet like?
2 How far has the spacecraft travelled?
3 How fast is the landing craft travelling when it enters the planet's atmosphere?
4 Why is a parachute used?
5 What happens to the landing craft on its way down?
6 What are used to slow the landing craft down for a gentle landing on the planet's surface?

B Copy the headings below and underneath them write the describing words (adjectives) used by the writer to describe the features of the planet.

sky	light	surface/ landscape
cloudless empty	strange pink	

volcanoes	deserts	canyons

C Put each of the following words (used in the passage on the opposite page) next to the definition that gives its meaning.

hover   equator   detach   orbit

1 _____ –to circle round a planet.
2 _____ –to unfasten, to set free.
3 _____ –to hang in the air.
4 _____ –an imaginary circle round a planet at an equal distance from its poles.

D Answer these questions about the information on the Viking space robots at the top of this page.

1 When did Viking 1 and Viking 2 land on Mars?
2 Why were the robots sent to the planet?
3 What sort of information did the robots send back?
4 Why is it likely that Mars has no forms of life at all?

E Discuss space exploration using the following points to help you.

1 It cost millions of dollars to send spacecraft to explore space. Do you think it is right to spend so much on space exploration when the money could be spent on solving some of the world's problems?
2 How does space exploration and the development of robots like Viking help mankind?

F Some ideas for writing.

1 Imagine you are a space explorer. You are landing on a strange, unknown planet. Describe its weird and fantastic landscape as you see it for the first time.
2 Write a story about a strange planet beginning, 'I was the first to step outside the landing craft.'
3 Write a funny story about a landing craft from a planet in outer space that touches down in your school playground or in the shopping centre.

It's your move

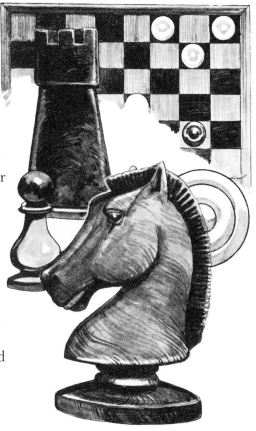

It's almost certain that you've heard of the game of Chess. You've probably heard of Draughts (or Checkers), and maybe of Ludo. But have you ever heard of Reversi, Shogi, Warlord, Senat, or Nine Men's Morris?

All these are games for two players and they have many things in common. In each game players move counters (or pieces) along lines or over squares, and one player tries to win, either by capturing his opponent's pieces or by trapping them so that they can't be moved.

Games like these are called games of *strategy*. Strategy means: to plan a series of moves that give you an advantage over your opponent.

Strategic games have been played for hundreds of years. Some of them were played by the Ancient Egyptians over two thousand years ago. It is known that the Vikings loved to play Chess and that Draughts is based on a game called Dames, invented in Southern France over eight hundred years ago.

Almost all the races of man play strategic games. Some are played on expensive gameboards bought in shops and stores. But most of these games were invented on lines or squares that were scratched into the ground or drawn on paper, the floor, or pavement with buttons, shells, coins, or even pebbles as playing pieces or counters.

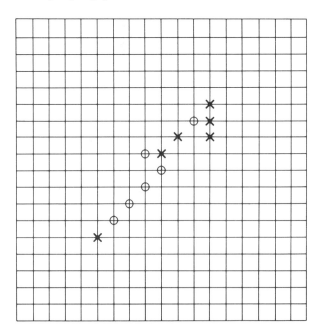

Gomuku

This simple game of strategy is an elaborate version of noughts and crosses. It is called *Gomuku* and is very popular in Japan. All you need is paper and a pencil. Draw an eighteen by eighteen square grid. Each player goes in turn and puts his nought (or cross) on one of the intersections on the grid. The aim of the game is to get five noughts or five crosses in a straight line in any direction. This is how the grid might look after both players have had their first six moves.

Hare and Hounds

This game is played all over the world. The Arizona Indians call it *Coyote and Chicken*. The Japanese call it *Soldiers' Eight-Way Hunt*.

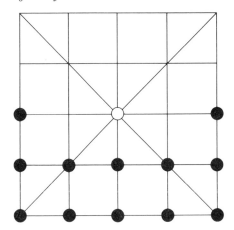

Here is how to play it.

1 The Hare player uses one counter. The Hounds player uses 12 of a different colour. Play takes place along all lines of the grid. Players go in turn.
2 The counters are placed as shown.
3 The Hare moves his counter to any next space. He may capture a hound if he is able to jump over one. He can only jump if the space beyond the hound is vacant for him to jump into. He may be able to capture two or more hounds if he can go on jumping in other directions.
4 The Hound player may move one of his counters in any direction also, one space per turn, but he may not jump or capture.
5 The Hare wins by capturing so many hounds that they cannot block him. The Hounds win if they block the Hare so that he can no longer move.

A Write sentences to answer these questions.

1 What does a chess board look like?
2 How many players are needed to play the games mentioned by the writer?
3 How does a player try to win when he plays these games?
4 What are games like these called?
5 Which game did the Vikings love to play?
6 What is the meaning of the word *strategy*?
7 What game is Draughts based on? When was that game invented?
8 What is it about strategic games that makes it easy for them to be played anywhere?

B Write out the following sentences putting the correct word from the list in each gap.

    plan   plot   strategy   tactics   idea

1 Everyone thought it was a good _____ to raise money to build a swimming pool.
2 The men were involved in a _____ to overthrow the government.
3 They decided to _____ an expedition that would take them round the world.
4 Because of the general's brilliant _____, the battle was easily won.
5 The captain discussed the _____ he wanted the team to use during the match.

C Copy the grids and play Gomuku, Hare and Hounds, or Kono. If you enjoy playing games of strategy like these, perhaps you could make proper boards and counters to play with.

Kono

This game for two players is popular in Korea. It is a game of manoeuvre, hide-and-seek, and deception.

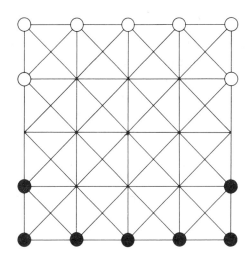

1 Each player uses seven counters of a different colour. These are placed on the grid as shown.
2 Each player at his turn moves one counter to any next empty space in any direction (up, back, across, or diagonally). He may also jump his own or his opponent's counters. But no counters are removed or captured at any time.
3 The idea of the game is to be first to occupy the opponent's home base with all counters—in a reversal of the starting position of the game.

REWARD

$700

REUBEN HUSTON BURROWS, alias RUBE BURROWS, charged with highway robbery. On the night of Friday, December 9, 1887, Reuben Burrows with his brother JAMES BUCHANAN BURROWS, and others, wearing masks, boarded the north bound train on the St. Louis, Arkansas & Texas Railroad and compelled the messenger of the SOUTHERN EXPRESS COMPANY to surrender the keys of his safe, which they rifled of $3,500. James Buchanan Burrows and three others of the robbers have since been arrested.

In an attempt to arrest Reuben Burrows and James Burrows in Montgomery, Alabama, on January 23, 1888, Reuben Burrows shot Mr Neil Bray who was aiding the officer in his arrest

DESCRIPTION

REUBEN HUSTON BURROWS is about 32 years of age, 6 feet in height, weighs about 160 pounds, blue eyes which do not look a person full in the face, round head, wears 7¼ hat, full forehead, face broad under the ears but thin near the mouth, a short (inclined to pug-shaped) nose, swarthy or sandy complexion, light sandy hair, uses Hair Oil to darken hair; left arm is a little shorter than the right, caused by having been broken at bend of arm; rather a lounging gait, carrying his hands in his pockets in a leisurely way.

Usually wears dark clothes and woollen shirts, boot size 8, wears no jewellery. Does not use tobacco; drinks, but not to excess; does not gamble, but can play the game of seven-up; is somewhat of a country story-teller, relating stories of snake, dog and cat fights etc. He is a good horseman, carries a .45 calibre pistol and is a good shot.

The Southern Express Company and the St. Louis Arkansas Railroad Co. have jointly offered a reward of five hundred dollars ($500) and in addition the Governor of the State of Arkansas has offered a reward of two hundred dollars ($200) for the arrest, delivery to the authorities and the conviction of Reuben Huston Burrows.

These are the points to keep in mind when you write a description of someone.

* approximate age of the person
* height, weight, and build
* shape of face, size and shape of nose
* colour of eyes
* colour and style of hair
* colour and shade of skin (complexion)
* features such as scar, mole, birthmark
* clothes, and style of dress
* mannerisms, habits, preferences
* any other important information

An identikit photo

A Write sentences to answer these questions.

1 For whom has the wanted poster been issued?
2 What crime has the wanted man committed?
3 When did the crime take place?
4 Describe Reuben Burrows' height and weight in your own words.
5 Write down a word which might describe the look of someone who will not look a person full in the face?
6 Describe Reuben Burrows' manner of walking in your own words.
7 What would you say was one of his mannerisms?
8 If Burrows put on a disguise and wore different clothes, in what other ways could he be recognized apart from his manner of walking?

B Here are a number of words which describe people's complexions

dark   pale   tanned   swarthy   sallow

Can you think of any more?

Here are a number of words which describe people's noses

long   flat   thin   sharp   up-turned

Can you think of any more?

Make a number of columns and write at the top of each one of the following headings

hair (colour)
hair (type and style)
eyes (colour and shape)
mouth and lips
skin and complexion
fingers and hands

Now make an identikit word chart using all the words you have collected, like this:

hair	hair	eyes	mouth	skin	fingers
blonde	straight	hazel	thin	smooth	short
black	curly	green	full	freckled	stubby
grey	short	small	narrow	pale	long

C Some ideas for writing.

Here is David's description of his friend Kevin.

> My friend Kevin is tall for his age. He is 5'7" and is the tallest boy in our class. He is quite thin and has large hands and feet. His face is long and narrow and he has thin lips and a sharp pointed nose. He has blue eyes and straight fair hair. He is always smiling and you can see he has a broken front tooth.
> He wears blue cord trousers and black trainers, and he has a dark blue sweater. He is good at football and he plays for the school team. His favourite football club is Nottingham Forest.

1 Write a description of your best friend, or of someone you know well.
2 Make a 'wanted' poster giving a full description of the wanted person.
3 Look for pictures of people's faces in magazines and newspapers. Cut them out and make a picture gallery. See how many words you can collect to describe the moods of the faces in your gallery. For example:

sad   angry   lonely   puzzled   frightened

On the ball

1 A metal mould is used with its interior formed to take the shape, in reverse, of the football's exterior. A polyvinyl chloride (PVC) paste is made up with PVC powder and a liquid plasticiser.

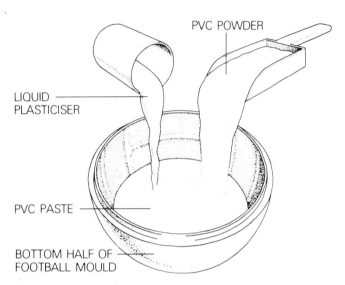

PVC POWDER

LIQUID PLASTICISER

PVC PASTE

BOTTOM HALF OF FOOTBALL MOULD

2 After the PVC has been poured into one half of the mould, the two halves are then assembled in a special way so that the mould can be spun through two axes. This is placed in an oven and heated to 150°C.

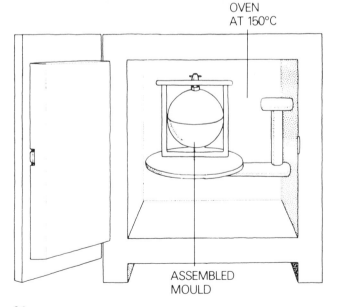

OVEN AT 150°C

ASSEMBLED MOULD

THE MOULD IS ROTATED IN TWO DIRECTIONS

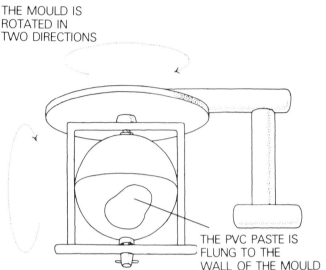

THE PVC PASTE IS FLUNG TO THE WALL OF THE MOULD

3 The mould is spun rapidly by an electric motor for a few minutes. The paste is flung outwards and forms an even, thin film over the inside of the mould.

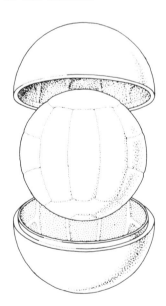

4 Under the action of the heat and the agitation, the paste sets into a rubber-like compound and remains in this state. After the mould has been removed from the oven and allowed to cool, it is opened and the finished football is removed.

Footballs have come a long way since the days when gangs of youths kicked an inflated pig's bladder through each other's villages toward goals that were often several miles apart.

Footballs today are very tough and, if they are not punctured, can stand up well to the hard treatment they get from school teams and other amateurs. Most balls are made of a plastic material called polyvinyl chloride (PVC). Regulation plastic balls have to be spherical in shape. They have to be approximately 685 mm. in circumference and weigh approximately 425 grams. Their pressure has to be equal to the atmospheric pressure at sea level.

A Write sentences to answer these questions.

1 What is the shape of the inside of the metal mould used to make a PVC football?
2 With what is the PVC paste made up?
3 Why is the PVC poured into one half of the mould only?
4 What does 'spun through two axes' mean?
5 Where does the spinning take place?
6 What happens to the PVC paste when the mould is spun?
7 What function does the oven have in the process?
8 When is the finished ball removed?

B The words in this list are similar in meaning. Copy out the sentences under the list putting the right word in each gap.

made produced assembled constructed invented

1 The Professor had _____ a machine for teaching mathematics to children while they were asleep.
2 The conjuror _____ a rabbit from a top hat.
3 The cook _____ a delicious meal of steak and chips followed by apple pie.
4 The boys checked all parts of the kit, then they _____ the model crane.
5 The engineers _____ a steel bridge to replace the old stone one.

C Answer these questions about the information at the top of this page.

1 From what were some of the very first footballs made?
2 Of what type of plastic are most modern footballs made?
3 What should the circumference of a regulation plastic ball be?
4 What should the weight of the regulation ball be?
5 Do you know of any drawbacks to a PVC ball?

D Keep these points in mind when you explain how to make something.

a The materials or ingredients you need
b The tools or equipment you need to use
c The way you make it (stage by stage)
d The finished product

Now explain how to make ANY of the following:

a cup of tea
a cooked breakfast
a camp fire
some home-made sweets
a greetings card
a Hallowe'en mask
a model
an indoor garden
a collection (stamps or coins)

The cat that helped make motoring safer

One dark foggy evening in 1933 a man was driving his car along a steep narrow road in Yorkshire. The road ran along the side of a steep hill. It was full of twists and bends. On one side of the road was a high bank of solid rock. On the other side was nothing, only a sheer drop.

The man often drove along this road. He thought he knew it well. But suddenly, just before a sharp bend, he ran into such thick fog that he could not see where he was going. He could not see the road and he could not tell how far he was from the edge.

At that very moment two pin-points of light shone through the fog. The car lights had been reflected in the eyes of a cat sitting on the fence. The cat's eyes had shown the man where the side of the road was and this had saved him from certain danger.

'What I need to help me home are hundreds of cats sitting along the road,' thought the man as he drove slowly on through the fog.

When at last the man reached the main road his lights shone on some metal tram lines that ran along the centre of the road. The man remembered the cat's eyes as he stared at the long line of gleaming tram lines. He began to think. Why not invent road studs with glass reflectors like cats' eyes in them? And why not set them in the middle of the road?

The man's name was Percy Shaw. Every motorist who has to drive at night is grateful to him. His invention—the catseye stud—has made roads and highways all over the world safer and easier to drive along after dark.

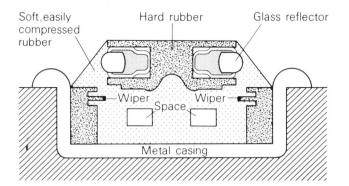

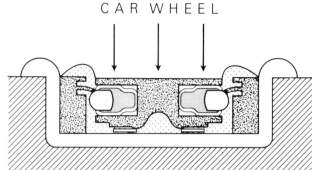

CAR WHEEL

How the catseyes are wiped.

Percy Shaw invented a catseye stud that would not be dangerous when run over by the wheel of a vehicle. The rubber would not get ripped or damaged. The glass reflectors would not get scratched or cracked and would also stay clean and free from mud and dirt. If you look at the diagram, you will see how this is done.

A Write sentences to answer these questions.

1 What kind of evening was it in 1933?
2 Why would a driver have to be careful when he drove along the road described in the article?
3 How did the man suddenly find himself in trouble?
4 What was it that saved him from certain danger?
5 What did the man think as he drove on?
6 What did he see when he reached the main road?
7 What idea did the man have?
8 What was the man's name, and how has his invention helped to make motoring safer?

B Here are two ways to use the word *reflect*:

a The still water *reflected* the full moon.
b The punishment he received made him *reflect* on the foolishness of what he had done.
Discuss these two meanings of reflect.

These words all have more than one meaning. Choose three and write two sentences for each one to show two different meanings:

smart   shoot   stalk   charge   prize   watch   light

C Answer the following questions about the diagram of the catseye studs at the top of this page.

1 Why do catseye studs have to stick up above the surface of the road?
2 If catseye studs were firm and solid, making little humps in the road surface:
a How might this be dangerous to road users?

b What would soon happen to the rubber casing?
c What would happen to the glass reflectors?
3 Study the diagram and say what happens to the studs when they are run over by the wheel of a vehicle.
4 Say how you think the glass 'eyes' are cleaned each time a vehicle runs over the stud.

D Explaining how things work.

Keep these points in mind when you explain how something works.
a The **purpose** of the object (what it is used for).
b The **materials** from which it is made.
c The **parts** of which it consists.
d The **function** (the way it works or operates).

Now explain how *any* of the following work:

a pen knife	a cheese grater
a bicycle reflector	a corkscrew
a drawing pin	a bicycle bell
a needle	a clothes peg
a safety pin	a bicycle pump
a screw driver	a tea bag.

E Discuss safety on the road at night, using the following points to help you.

1 Apart from catseye studs, what other sorts of reflectors and reflective surfaces help road users?
2 What does the law say a cyclist must have on his bicycle when he cycles after dark?
3 In what other ways should a cyclist make himself clearly visible at night?

Would you know what to do?

You probably know how painful it can be to have a small burn or scald. Burns and scalds are the most common type of accident in the home. If you had to deal with a *bad* burn or scald, would *you* know what to do?

If you touch anything very hot, like a hot iron or hot cooker, you *burn* your skin. Burns are caused by DRY heat.

If your skin contacts steam or very hot water, you will *scald* yourself. Scalds are caused by WET heat.

If someone has a large burn or scald it is very painful. The shock and pain from the burn may affect the whole body and the person may become very ill.

The first thing to do is to cool the skin with cold water. The burn or scald causes pain and damage because of the heat. The damage and pain can be made less if the burned or scalded skin is made cooler.

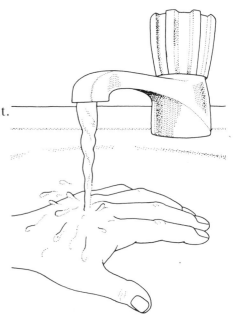

Act quickly. Don't wait until a sink or bath has filled up. Pour the cold water on the injury at once. Don't stop to remove clothing from the injured person, or worry about spilling water on the floor or carpet.

It takes a long time to get the heat out of an injured part of the body, so you must go on cooling it for at least ten minutes.

Often, in a burn or a scald, the injured part will swell up. So you must take off anything tight, like a watch or a shoe, before the swelling gets too bad. Do this while you are cooling the wound with cold water.

Cooling the burn does three things:

It helps to stop the heat damaging the skin any more.
It helps to make the pain less.
It also helps to make the injured part swell less.

If a blister comes up where the skin has been burned or scalded never prick it or break it. Do not even touch it.

Do not put ointment or cream on skin which is burned or scalded.

Call a grown-up as quickly as you can. Let a grown-up decide whether to call a doctor or take the injured person to hospital.

AMBULANCE

A Write sentences to answer these questions.

1 What is a burn? How is it caused?
2 What is a scald? How is it caused?
3 Why may someone with a large burn or scald become ill?
4 What is the first thing you MUST do when a person has been burned or scalded?
5 Why is it so important to cool the skin?
6 How long should you go on cooling the injured part?
7 What precautions should you take in case the injured part swells up?

B Answer these questions from the information at the top of this page.

1 What should you never do to a blister on burned or scalded skin?
2 What three things do cooling the skin help?
3 What should you never put on a burn or scald?
4 What will a grown-up be able to decide?
5 Why would calling a grown-up not be the very first thing you would do?
6 If you couldn't find a grown-up, what would you have to decide for yourself?

C What did they do wrong?

Write down all the mistakes that John and his mother made when Karen scalded herself.

One Saturday afternoon, John and Karen were making a cup of tea. Suddenly Karen accidentally poured some boiling water over her wrist and scalded herself badly.

John rushed off at once to find their mother. 'Quickly, Karen's scalded herself,' he shouted.

Karen's mother ran into the kitchen. 'Take your watch off and put your wrist under the cold tap while I look for the first-aid box,' she ordered.

Karen held her hand under the tap for two or three minutes. 'The water takes away a lot of the pain,' she said, dabbing her wrist dry with the kitchen towel.

A blister had come up on Karen's skin. 'I'd better pop that blister,' said Karen's mother. 'Then I'll put some soothing cream on it.'

D Discuss first aid using the following points to help you.

1 How do you make an emergency phone-call for the ambulance?
2 Why should every home have a first-aid kit? What items do you think should be in it?
3 What other essential first aid should everyone know?
4 Everyone should know how to put an unconscious person in the recovery position. Find out who knows how to do this and get them to show you.

E What precautions should you take when doing any of the following:

1 Filling a hot water bottle from a kettle.
2 Pouring boiling water into a teapot.
3 Boiling water in a saucepan on a stove.
4 Filling a kettle soon after it has had boiling water in it.

The mystery at Swiftmouth Bay

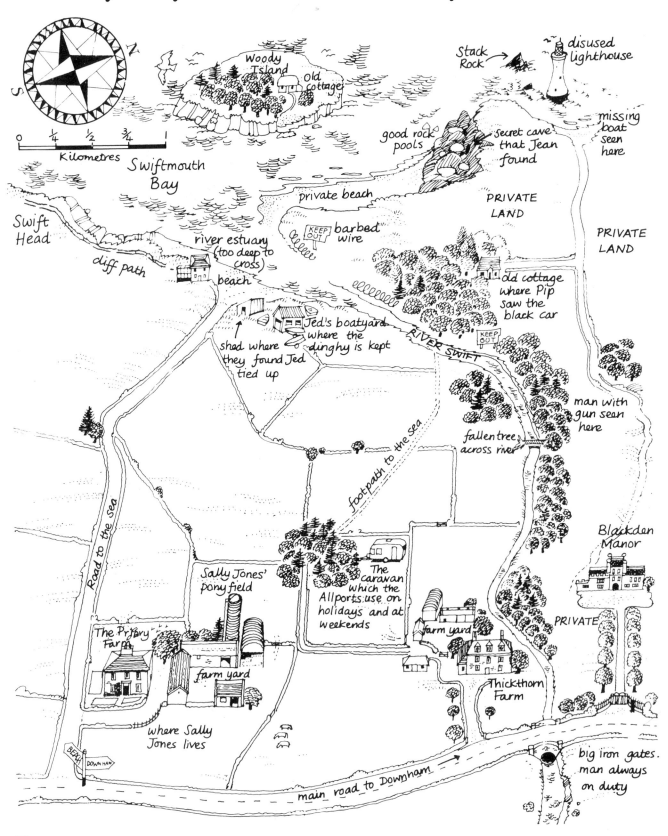

Woody Island
Old cottage

Stack Rock

disused lighthouse

good rock pools

Secret cave that Jean found

missing boat seen here

PRIVATE LAND

PRIVATE LAND

Swiftmouth Bay

private beach

KEEP OUT barbed wire

Swift Head

cliff path

river estuary (too deep to cross)

beach

old cottage where Pip saw the black car

KEEP OUT

shed where they found Jed tied up

Jed's boatyard where the dinghy is kept

RIVER SWIFT

man with gun seen here

fallen tree across river

footpath to the sea

Blackden Manor

Road to the sea

Sally Jones' pony field

The caravan which the Allports use on holidays and at weekends

farm yard

PRIVATE

The Priory Farm

farm yard

Thickthorn Farm

where Sally Jones lives

BEACH DOWNHAM

main road to Downham

big iron gates. man always on duty

0   ¼   ½   ¾   1
Kilometres

Characters

PIP JEAN ALEC MRS ALLPORT SALLY JED

A Write sentences to answer these questions.

1 What are the names of the Allport children?
2 Where do the Allports keep their caravan?
3 How can you tell that not many holidaymakers visit Swiftmouth Bay?
4 Where does Sally Jones live?
5 Why do you think that Sally is glad when the Allport children come to stay?
6 What does Jed do for a living?
7 Where do the Allports keep their dinghy?
8 How can you tell that Blackden Manor is a strange place?
9 Why is it not possible to walk to the rock pools?
10 Which *two* ways could the children get to the rock pools?

B Answer these questions briefly.

1 How far is it direct from the caravan to Jed's boatyard?
2 How big is Woody Island?
3 How far is it along the private beach from the estuary to the secret cave?
4 About how far is Blackden Manor from the secret cave in a straight line?
5 In which direction is Downham?

C Think about and discuss possible answers to the following questions using the map to help you. There are no 'correct' answers. Make up your own story.

1 Why do you think the children wanted to go to the rock pools?
2 What do you think they found in the secret cave?
3 Why do you think they explored the Blackden Estate?
4 Why do you think a man had a gun?
5 Why do you think Jed was tied up?
6 Why would the fallen tree across the river be useful?
7 What could Woody Island or the disused lighthouse have been used for?
8 Why do you think the boat was taken?
9 Where do you think the nearest police station is?

D Some ideas for writing.

1 Write the story of 'The Mystery at Swiftmouth Bay'.
2 Write a mystery story of your own, and illustrate it with a map.

Can you solve it?

A's bill			
TOTAL		£1-90	
12			
SOUP			
FISH	✓	I	30
MEAT			
VEGETABLE	✓		40
SWEET			
CHEESE			
COFFEE/TEA	✓		20
CAKES			
SOFT DRINKS			
CIGARETTES			
☐		I	90
Thank You			

B's bill			
TOTAL		— 20	
11			
SOUP			
FISH			
MEAT			
VEGETABLE			
SWEET			
CHEESE			
COFFEE/TEA	✓		20
CAKES			
SOFT DRINKS			
CIGARETTES			
☐			20
Thank You			

C's bill			
TOTAL		£3-35	
13			
SOUP			
FISH			
MEAT	✓	I	60
VEGETABLE	✓		80
SWEET			
CHEESE			
COFFEE/TEA	✓		20
CAKES			
SOFT DRINKS			
CIGARETTES	✓		75
☐		3	35
Thank You			

D's bill			
TOTAL		£1-90	
14			
SOUP			
FISH	✓	I	30
MEAT			
VEGETABLE	✓		40
SWEET			
CHEESE			
COFFEE/TEA	✓		20
CAKES			
SOFT DRINKS			
CIGARETTES			
☐		I	90
Thank You			

On the opposite page you will see a sketch of Martha's Café three minutes after a shooting incident. Police were called to the café seconds after the shot was fired. They found exactly what you see.

The victim was identified as 'Mugsy' Morrow, a well-known gangster and criminal. The murderer had leaned against the wall while firing at point-blank range. His gloved hand left a mark on the wall which can be clearly seen. Martha could tell the police nothing except that Morrow must have walked into the café just before nine o'clock and been shot by one of the customers. She could not say which one had done the shooting.

With these facts in mind study the scene and see if you can identify the murderer. Then answer the questions to help you decide who the killer was.

Look at the picture and the bills above and answer the following questions by deciding which is the correct answer. The first two have been done to show the type of reason you should have for your answer. You need not write your reasons out.

1 Had Martha been washing the floor?
☐ Yes   ☐ No
Yes. You can see a pail and mop, and the floor is wet.

2 How many customers had been using the cafe?
☐ None   ☐ One   ☐ Two   ☐ Three
☐ Four   ☐ Five
Four. There are four bills and four places which show that people have been eating at the cafe.

3 Were all the customers still in the cafe when Morrow walked in?
☐ Yes   ☐ No

4 Would footsteps show if they had not been on the wet floor?
☐ Yes   ☐ No

5 Which are Martha's footsteps?
☐ X   ☐ Y   ☐ Z

6 Did Martha go through to the kitchen?
☐ Yes   ☐ No

7 Did she ring up the 20p bill on the till before the murder?
☐ Yes   ☐ No

8 Where was Martha at the moment of shooting?
☐ By the till   ☐ In the kitchen

9 Which are A's footsteps?
☐ X   ☐ Y   ☐ Z

10 Did A run out through the kitchen door?
☐ Yes   ☐ No

11 Are the footsteps marked X those of the murderer?
☐ Yes   ☐ No

12 In which hand did the murderer hold his gun?
☐ Right   ☐ Left

13 Which two customers are left-handed?
☐ B   ☐ C   ☐ D

14 Which customers smoke cigarettes?
☐ A   ☐ B   ☐ C   ☐ D

15 Was anything dropped on the floor after it had been washed by Martha?
☐ Yes   ☐ No

16 Who killed Mugsy Morrow?
☐ A   ☐ B   ☐ C   ☐ D

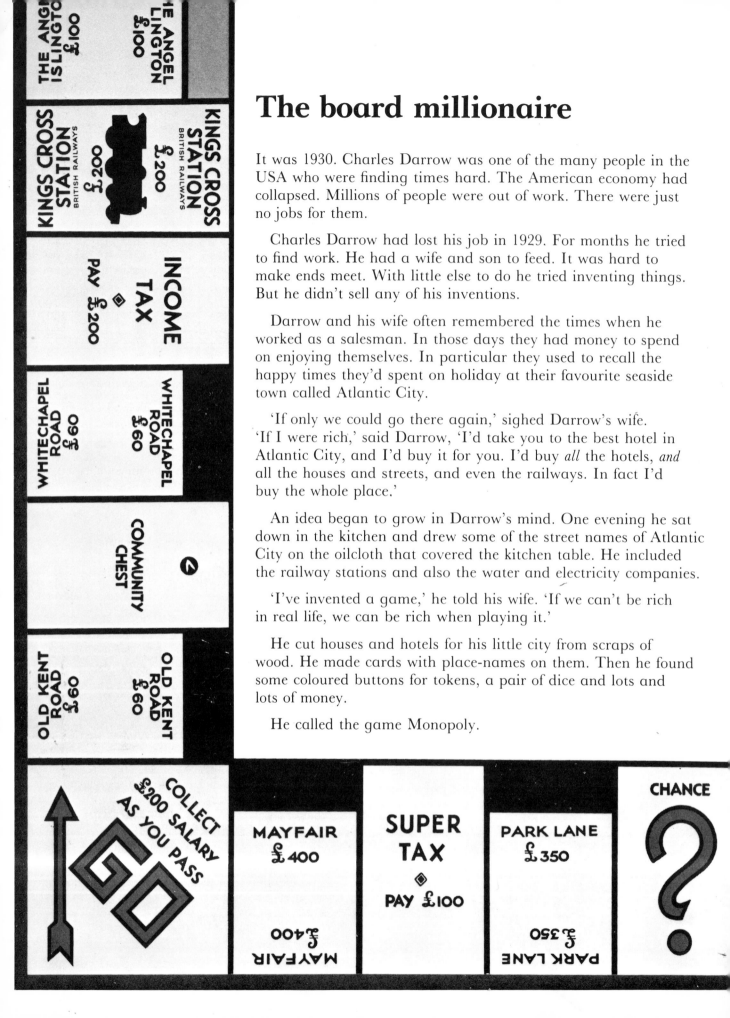

The board millionaire

It was 1930. Charles Darrow was one of the many people in the USA who were finding times hard. The American economy had collapsed. Millions of people were out of work. There were just no jobs for them.

Charles Darrow had lost his job in 1929. For months he tried to find work. He had a wife and son to feed. It was hard to make ends meet. With little else to do he tried inventing things. But he didn't sell any of his inventions.

Darrow and his wife often remembered the times when he worked as a salesman. In those days they had money to spend on enjoying themselves. In particular they used to recall the happy times they'd spent on holiday at their favourite seaside town called Atlantic City.

'If only we could go there again,' sighed Darrow's wife. 'If I were rich,' said Darrow, 'I'd take you to the best hotel in Atlantic City, and I'd buy it for you. I'd buy *all* the hotels, *and* all the houses and streets, and even the railways. In fact I'd buy the whole place.'

An idea began to grow in Darrow's mind. One evening he sat down in the kitchen and drew some of the street names of Atlantic City on the oilcloth that covered the kitchen table. He included the railway stations and also the water and electricity companies.

'I've invented a game,' he told his wife. 'If we can't be rich in real life, we can be rich when playing it.'

He cut houses and hotels for his little city from scraps of wood. He made cards with place-names on them. Then he found some coloured buttons for tokens, a pair of dice and lots and lots of money.

He called the game Monopoly.

Monopoly is a game where players travel round a board at the throw of two dice. The idea of the game is for a player to get very rich by buying streets and putting houses and hotels on them. Then if other players land on those streets, they have to pay enormous sums of money in rent.

Monopoly is the world's best-selling board game. By 1982 almost a hundred-million sets had been sold in the USA alone. The game is sold in twenty-five countries and has been translated into fifteen languages.

Monopoly made Charles Darrow a very wealthy man. He never had to look for work again. He became a gentleman farmer in Pennsylvania and used to travel all over the world.

A Write sentences to answer these questions.

1 What problem were millions of Americans in the USA facing in 1930?
2 Why was Charles Darrow finding times hard?
3 How did Charles Darrow spend his time?
4 Why did Darrow and his wife often talk about Atlantic City?
5 What did Darrow say he would do if he were rich?
6 On what did Darrow draw his game?
7 On what city did he base the game?
8 What can players pretend or imagine when they play Monopoly?

B
Mono- comes from the Greek word *monos* meaning *only, alone, single*

monopoly means—the *only* person with the right to sell something, having complete control of it.

Here are four words beginning with *mono*, and pictures of each one. Write down what each one means.

monogram, monoplane, monorail, monocle.

C Rewrite these five sentences making *one* sentence of only 23 words.

Monopoly is a game.
It is a board game.
It is a game for up to six people.
It is a game in which players travel round a board.
They travel round at the throw of two dice.

D For discussion.

Sometimes people like to daydream and imagine they are very, very rich. Supposing you were given £100,000,000. Talk about what you would do with it.

E Make a board game.

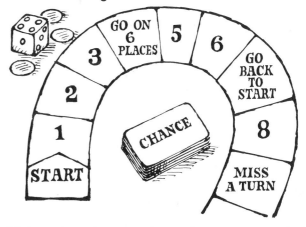

Make a board game where players go round a course at the throw of a dice. Make some squares help a player and some hold him up or send him back. You may be able to think of extra ways, like *chance cards* to make your game more fun.

Every picture tells a story

1

2

3

4

5

Together these pictures make a story, but if you think about it it's a story which can be told in many different ways. Think about and discuss your answers to all the questions on this page. There are no 'correct' answers. Make up your own story.

A What is happening in picture 1?

Discuss why one boy is in the boat and the other boy is not.
Could there be reasons why the boy on the jetty doesn't want to go off in the boat?
Could there be reasons why the boy in the boat doesn't want the other one to come?
Could the boy on the jetty be scared for some reason?
What if the boat doesn't belong to the boys?
What if the boat belongs to the boy on the jetty but *not* to the boy in the boat?

B What is happening in picture 2?

Is the boy in the boat being foolish?
What might he be thinking?
What has happened to the boy who stayed behind?
Has he seen how far out the other boy has gone?
What if he has gone home to watch TV?
Why might he not want anything to do with the boy in the boat?

C What is happening in picture 3?

Discuss what happens when a storm begins.
What happens to the sun?
What do the clouds do?
What happens to the wind?

What does the wind do to leaves and scraps of paper?
What does the wind do to the sea?
What does it do when it rains?

D What is happening in picture 4?

Think of a storm at sea. How many storm verbs can you think of?

What is a *lull* in a storm?
What is meant by 'the lull before the storm'?
What *might* have happened to the boat?
What might the boy on shore do when he saw the storm?
What *ought* he to do?
Why might he be too scared to phone the coastguard?

E What is happening in picture 5?

Did the story have a happy ending?

F Some ideas for writing.

1 Write your own version of the story making each picture a chapter.
2 Write a story of your own about a rescue at sea.
3 Write a story about two children who have an argument and one gets into danger.

Getting it right

Miss Fawcett's class were looking at some of the new books that had come in from the library van. One of the books had a picture of a Roman soldier. 'There's something wrong with this picture,' said Margaret Roxon. 'Legionary soldiers didn't look like this.'

A FIRST-CENTURY ROMAN LEGIONARY

The illustration of a Roman legionary soldier that Margaret Roxon found was hopelessly wrong.

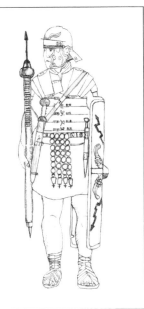

LEGIONARIES

Legionaries were highly trained Roman soldiers. A legionary had to be a Roman citizen. He had to serve for 25 years. It was the ambition of every Legionary to become a centurion

From the middle of the first century, they wore plate armour. This was made from a series of curved metal plates. The plates over lapped and were held together by hinges, hooks and straps.

The helmet had hinged side-flaps to protect the face, and had a large peak at the back.

A legionary carried a curved, rectangular shield (scutum) and a javelin (pilum). The pilum had a wooden handle with a slender metal head which was barbed at the tip.

He wore a sword belt which had the sword on his right side and a dagger on his left.

Here is a page from Peter Connolly's project on first-century Roman soldiers.

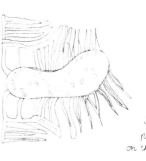

This is an example of a Roman military sandal (caliga).

The upper part was cut from a single piece of leather which wrapped around the foot and was sewn up at the heel. This was attached to a heavy sole made of several layers of leather. The sole was shod with iron studs.

The iron studs made this type of sandal very slippery when walking on stone pavements. Josephus describes a centurion dashing across the paved temple courtyard at Jerusalem, skidding on the iron studs, and falling flat on his back.

A page from Mary Worrall's project on footwear through the ages.

Here is a page from Micky Poulton's project book. Look at his drawings of three other sorts of Roman soldier. These are all correctly drawn.

auxiliary

legate

1st century praetorian guard

A Can you get it right?

1 Use the information from Peter Connolly's project on Roman soldiers, and Mary Worrall's project on footwear to decide what is wrong with the picture of the legionary. Write a list of all the wrong things that you find.

2 Look at the three drawings of Roman soldiers drawn by Micky Poulton. The legionary has something from all of them. Write down what these are.

B The word *wrong* has several meanings. Copy out the sentences putting the most suitable word from the list in the place of the word *wrong*.

dishonest   incorrect   unsuitable   reverse   faulty

1 If your answers are *wrong*, you will fail the test.
2 Cheating is always *wrong*.
3 There's something *wrong* with this engine.
4 This wallpaper is *wrong* for a baby's nursery.
5 Iron the material on the *wrong* side.

C Look at the information on military footwear on the opposite page and answer the following questions.

1 How do you think the Roman military sandal was done up or fastened?

2 Why do you think it had so many loops and just two or three thick wide straps?
3 What do you think would be the advantage of the military sandal?
4 What might be its disadvantages?

D Are you good at spotting mistakes? All the following have at least one error, some have several. Discuss each one and say what the mistakes are.

1 The peacock flew into the neighbour's garden and laid its eggs in the long grass there.

2 Last year the milkman never failed to call at our house. He came long before we were up. Think of it, every day, for 356 days of the year, as the sun rose in the west, he set out with his milk float and finished his round before we even got to school.

3 The British flag is called the Union Flag. It consists of three flags: the flag of St. George of England—a red cross on a white background; the flag of St. Patrick of Scotland—a blue diagonal cross on a white background; and the flag of St. Andrew of Ireland—a red diagonal cross on a white background.

Human statistics

	Normal	Maximum	Minimum
Height	Men: 1.28m.–2.01m. (4′ 3″–6′ 7″) Women: 1.18m.–1.87m. (3′ 11″–6′ 1½″)	The tallest man on record was Robert Wadlow of Illinois, USA, who reached a height of 2.72m. (8′ 11″). At the age of 8 he was 1.8m. (6′ 0″) tall. He died in 1940.	The shortest person on record was a Dutch midget called Pauline Musters. Just before her death at the age of 19, she measured .61m. (2′).
Weight	Men: 51–92 kg. (8–14½ st.) Women: 38–79 kg. (6½–12½ st.)	Robert Earl Hughes of Missouri, USA, weighed 483 kg. (76 st. 5 lb.) Hughes died in 1958 and was buried in a coffin the size of a piano crate.	The lightest adult human on record was Lucia Zarate. Born in Mexico in 1863, she weighed only 5.9 kg. (13 lb.) on her 20th birthday.
Number of hairs on head	120,000 (average)	Natural blondes can have as many as 140,000.	The minimum (not counting baldness) is among redheads, who can have as few as 90,000.
Sleep needed per day	7–9 hours (adults) 8–11 hours (children)	New-born babies require 18–20 hours a day.	Older people may get along on as little as 5 hours a day.
Body temperature	36°–37°C (97°–99°F)	Patients are likely to die if their temperature rises above 43°C (110°F). Doctors once saved the life of a woman whose temperature reached 44°C (112°F).	At 26.4°C (79.5°F) the heart fails. A 2-year-old girl who was found in an unheated house during a Chicago winter recovered from a temperature of 16.0°C (60.8°F).
Bones	206 in the human body	The thigh bone (or femur) is the longest bone in the body.	The stirrup bone (or stapes) in the middle ear is the smallest.
Heartbeats per minute	60–85 (when resting)	In young people during strenuous exercise, the heart may beat as often as 270 times a minute.	50–60 during sleep
Size of babies at birth	2.72–3.6 kg. (6–8 lb.)	The biggest baby on record was a 10.8 kg. (23 lb. 12 oz.) boy born to a 2.13m. (7′6″) Nova Scotian giantess Mrs Anna Bates.	The smallest baby known to have survived is a 183 g. (10 oz) girl born in South Shields in 1938.

Brain—the human brain is 80% water.

Breathing—we normally breathe sixteen to eighteen times a minute. In twenty-four hours we breathe in about 11.23 cubic metres (400 cubic feet) of air.

Hair—no matter what colour our hair is it all grows at the rate of 0.43 mm. (0.01714 in.) in twenty-four hours.

Nail—there is enough iron in the human body to make a nail.

Skin—The complete skin covering the human body would cover an area of about 1.85 sq. metres. (20 sq. feet). It would weigh 2.72 kg. (6 lb.) when bundled together.

A Write sentences to answer these questions.

1 Who is recorded as the tallest man in the world? How tall was he?
2 Which is the longest bone in the human body?
3 How often does a normal heart beat when a person is asleep?
4 What is the average number of hairs on a person's head?
5 Which type of person has the least number of hairs?
6 How much did Lucia Zarate weigh on her 20th birthday?
7 How much sleep do new-born babies require?
8 How many bones does the human body have?
9 What is the normal body temperature?
10 What normally happens if the body temperature drops below 26.4°C (79.5°F)?

B Record-breaker words
Complete this table of comparisons.

describing word	comparison of two	of more than two
small	smaller	smallest
big	_____	biggest
bright	brighter	_____
slow	_____	_____
fast	_____	_____

some more difficult comparisons

good	better	_____
much	_____	_____
little	_____	_____
bad	_____	_____

C Complete the following sentences by using the right form of the word in the brackets.

1 Mark is _____ than John. (tall)
2 David is the _____ boy in the class. (big)
3 Of the two girls, Mandy runs _____ than Karen. (fast)
4 The Pacific is the _____ ocean in the world. (large)
5 My right eye is the _____ one. (weak)

Some more difficult ones:

1 Measure them both and tell me which is the _____. (long)
2 Who did _____ work; Sue, Mandy or Diane? (more or most)
3 Of all the stories I liked this one; it had the _____ excitement. (more or most?)

D Use the chart opposite and the information at the top of this page to make up six more questions of your own. Write the questions down, but do not write the answers.

E Collect statistics about all the members of your class or group. Display the results using charts and graphs. Use them to make a wall display.

F Make up a quiz of your own based on amazing facts.

Chariot
holidays for young people

What to bring

No expensive clothing or equipment is required. A detailed list of clothing and other requisites is included in the holiday final information leaflet. A sample list for one week at a Chariot holiday in the UK is given below for your guidance.

Pillow

Two warm jerseys

Three shirts, blouses or T shirts

Two pairs of jeans

Two bathing suits

Several pairs of socks

Canvas or plastic shoes for watersports

Wellington boots

Stout shoes for walking and/or trekking

Waterproof bags

Torch, string etc.

Toilet bag and contents

Towels

Riding and Pony Trekking at Poulton Court
AGE RANGE 10–14

Poulton Court, once a large vicarage, stands on the edge of Exmoor in ten acres of grounds including a garden, fields, and a stream. The facilities include two shower rooms, a dining room, and a recreation room. Accommodation is in large bedrooms for a total of about 40 boys and girls.

This riding holiday will include 4 days' riding. As well as trekking on Exmoor and in the lovely Coombe Valley, time will be spent on developing riding skills and on gymkhana games. In addition there will be lectures and practical experience with horses and the care of ponies.

Our specially trained staff ensure that everyone, from beginner to experienced rider, receives the very best attention.

Football Coaching at Tabbener's School
AGE RANGE 9–12

This year's five-day football coaching holiday for the 9–12 year age-range will be held at Tabbener's School, near Wharton in Sussex. The school offers a good range of facilities with excellent playing fields and an indoor swimming pool. Accommodation is in 5–9 bedded rooms, while the school's cooks provide good quality meals.

The coaching courses are staffed by carefully selected coaches. Children on each course are split into groups according to age and ability so that each boy or girl is coached in the many aspects of the game to his or her fullest ability.

There is an opportunity to take part in games of soccer as well as training sessions and indoor five-a-side football. Soccer coaching films are shown in the evenings as additional training aids. There is also a visit to the ground of a league club, and on one afternoon of the week, a star player attends the course to take a coaching session.

Every participant on this course will be expected to bring two sets of football kit, a pair of football boots and training shoes.

SAMPLE PROGRAMME

DAY	MORNING	AFTERNOON	EVENING
MON	Arrive	Basic kicking ball control	Training film
TUE	Shooting/ heading	Dribbling/ tackling	Five-a-side competition
WED	Small games/ grid training	Visit to a League Club	Five-a-sides
THUR	Attacking skills	Defending skills	Training Film/ Game
FRI	Coaching by a star player	Awards and Certificates	— —
SAT	Depart		

SAMPLE PROGRAMME

DAY	MORNING	AFTERNOON	EVENING
SAT		Arrive	Scavenger Hunt
SUN	Instruction on tack cleaning and grooming	Trek	Film
MON	Lecture on pony care	Valley trek	Campfire
TUE	All day trek	——	Swimming/ games
WED	Grooming/ care	Swimming Tennis	Barbecue
THUR	All day moorland trek		Quiz
FRI	Trek	Gymkhana	Disco
SAT	Depart		

Multi-activity Adventure Holiday at Craigthorpe Castle
AGE RANGE 9–13

Craigthorpe Castle is the ideal setting for this multi-activity holiday. Set in superb grounds overlooking the hills of Invergary and the River Trune, the centre includes an indoor heated swimming pool, gymnasiums, tennis courts, air-rifle range, and woodland assault course. And there is easy access to Loch Argh for sailing and canoeing.

All this goes with the fun of staying in a real Scottish castle with its magnificent panelled great hall, dungeons, battlements and oak staircases complete with suits of armour.

Accommodation is in 2–6 bedded rooms with every modern facility. Meals are taken in the great dining hall. Food is excellent, and the first-class menu includes a 'banquet' in the great hall on the last evening.

Chariot Activity Leaders ensure that children enjoy a wide choice of activities. Trained instructors are on hand to ensure that each child participates with maximum enjoyment and safety. Evening activities include a dungeon disco, ghost hunt, and recreation rooms.

SAMPLE PROGRAMME

DAY	MORNING	AFTERNOON	EVENING
SAT		Arrive	Film of activities
SUN	Rifle range	Gymnasium or ball courts	Outdoor game
MON	Canoeing or sailing	Assault course	Dungeon disco
TUES	Expedition	Rifle range	Mini Olympics
WED	Gymnasium or swimming sports	Canoeing or sailing	It's a knockout
THUR	Nature trail	Pony riding	Ghost hunt
FRI	Hill walk	Tennis or swimming	Banquet
SAT	Depart		

Buntin's Holiday Camp

Hundreds of children over the years have enjoyed a fun-packed, please-yourself Chariot holiday at the ever popular Buntin Holiday Camp near Exton in South Devon.

All the fun of a Buntin holiday is provided, but with one difference—children don't have their parents there to worry about!

Accommodation is in 2–4 bedded chalets with all modern facilities. Popular cafeteria meals are available at midday and early evening.

As well as unlimited use of the heated swimming pool, go-kart track, roller-skating rink and indoor inflatable, there is a wide variety of organized games. These include a treasure hunt, crazy sports, a frisbee marathon, it's a knockout, and a custard pie contest.

Evening activities include a talent show, disco and modern dancing, sing-along and comedy concert. There is also a full day excursion to the seaside.

Despite the free-and-easy atmosphere, all activities are closely supervised by Chariot Holiday Group Leaders and Buntin Stripecoats.

A Four holidays are described on the preceding pages. Choose any *one* of them and answer the following questions.

1 What did you like about the holiday that made you choose it?
2 What kind of activities does your holiday offer?
3 Which activity do you think you would enjoy the most, and why?
4 Which activity do you think you would enjoy the least and why?
5 What do you like most about your particular holiday centre?
6 Look at the 'What to bring' section. What other important items should you take that are not included on the list?

B Each word in the left-hand column has one of similar meaning in the right-hand column. Copy the words out putting them in their correct pairs:

holiday	pursuit
activity	make certain
ensure	coach
instructor	take part
participate	utmost
maximum	vacation

C There are lots of advantages to organized activity holidays although maybe you've never been on one.
Even so, what do you think would be *most* important about such a holiday? Write down the items in this list *in order of importance*. For example if you think 'good food' is most important, put it first.

* going with a friend or friends
* having plenty of free time
* taking part in new activities
* having first-class accommodation
* a choice of things to do
* learning from experts
* close supervision by grown-ups
* good food

Give a reason for your choice of first item.

D Discuss supervised activity holidays using the following points to help you.

1 What do you think you might gain from such a holiday?
2 What are the most important aspects of such a holiday that would make it really enjoyable?
3 Compare your list of importance with others in the class and discuss it.
4 What are the main differences between the activities in the first three holidays, and the one at Buntin holiday camp?

E Some ideas for writing.

1 Write a letter home from the activity centre you have chosen describing some of the things you have been doing.
2 Plan an activity holiday by writing out a sample programme based on your own or a particular hobby or activity e.g. a *nature* holiday, or a *music* holiday.
3 Make up a holiday and write a funny description with a sample programme for a ghosts' holiday at Doom Hall or Creaky Castle.
4 Write a week's sample programme for a Chariot holiday at Count Dracula's Castle amid the sinister scenery of Transylvania.

Shipwrecked

This is an exercise in which you will have to use your imagination and have a good deal of discussion before you come to any decisions. The exercise is set in the past because it seems more likely that a galleon would carry all the equipment in the list you are asked to consider.

June 7th, 1739. Your galleon has been driven on to a coral reef during a violent storm. All the crew have been washed over-board and drowned except you and one other person. Now the ship is breaking up and you will lose your life if you don't launch the raft you have managed to make and get to the island about half a mile away.

The island is a tropical paradise. It is uninhabited, but it has fruit, wild animals (such as goats and pigs), birds, fish, turtles, and fresh water.

With you and your companion on board, the raft will only carry 30 kilograms of equipment. So you will have to choose what to take and what to leave behind. If you decide to swim and tow the raft, you will be able to take the equivalent of your body weight in extra equipment (but watch out for killer sharks if you do).

Here is a list of the items you can take. Everything on the list will be useful but decide which items you think you would need most of all and total up the weights. Remember the raft will sink if you overload it.

Equipment

tool kit (total weight 6 kg.)

containing:

hammer	½ kg. (0.5 kg.)
saw	½ kg. (0.5 kg.)
nails (in boxes)	½ kg. (0.5 kg.)
chisels	¼ kg. (0.25 kg.)
wood plane	¾ kg. (0.75 kg.)
crowbar	1 kg.

dry flour (in sacks)	4 kg. each
molasses (sugar in barrels)	3 kg. each
lard (in barrels)	3 kg. each
brandy (in barrels)	10 kg. each
brandy (in bottles)	1 kg. each
spare sea-boots	4 kg.
spare clothes	2½ kg. (2.5 kg.)

medicine chest
(total weight 1½ kg.)　　(1.5 kg.)

containing:

iodine (strong antiseptic)	½ kg. (0.5 kg.)
bandages	½ kg. (0.5 kg.)
swabs, splints etc.	¼ kg. (0.25 kg.)
pins, needles, clamps	¼ kg. (0.25 kg.)

seeds (in sacks)

corn	5 kg.
maize (sweet corn)	2 kg.
oats	3 kg.
potatoes	5 kg.

canvas (spare sails)	8 kg.
blankets	1½ kg. (1.5 kg.) each
hammock	3 kg.

compass	½ kg. (0.5 kg.)
sextant	½ kg. (0.5 kg.)
sailmaker's kit (needles, twine, bodkins)	1 kg.
pots and pans (would float with lids on)	
gunpowder (in sealed casks)	10 kg.
shot for the gun (boxes)	2 kg. each
gun	1½ kg. (1.5 kg.)
axe	1 kg.
flints and dry tinder	½ kg. (0.5 kg.)
ship's cat (still alive)	1 kg.
spade	2 kg.
hoe	1 kg.
pickaxe	3½ kg. (3.5 kg.)
ship's log book	½ kg. (0.5 kg.)
Bible	1 kg.
ink and pens	¼ kg. (0.25 kg.)
telescope	½ kg. (0.5 kg).
rope (50 metres)	6 kg.
string and twine	1 kg.
knife	¼ kg. (0.25 kg.)
butchers knife	1 kg.
machete (jungle knife)	1 kg.
grindstone (for sharpening)	1 kg.

A Congratulations on reaching the island safely with your equipment. After you have seen to the urgent needs of food and shelter, you will probably want to explore the island. Draw a map of the island when you have done this, marking on it all the features such as hills, woodland, shores, and reefs. You may like to give them names.

B Write the story (or a daily record such as a log book) of your first week on the island.

Acknowledgements

The publishers would like to thank the following for permission to reproduce photographs:

Butlins Ltd., p. 45; Camera Press, p. 38 (top right); J. Allan Cash, p. 38 (bottom left and right); Fiat Auto (UK) Ltd., p. 18 (bottom); McLeish Associates Ltd., p. 18 (top); The National Trust, p. 8; Oxford Mail, p. 27; PGL Young Adventure Ltd., p. 44 (top and bottom); Royal National Lifeboat Institution, p. 39; Space Frontiers Ltd., p. 21; St. John Ambulance, p. 31; Thames Valley Police, p. 25; J. Thomas, p. 38 (top left); Waddington's Games Ltd., p. 36.

Illustrations are by Patricia Capon, Peter Dennis, Terence Gabbey, David Hunt. John Hunt, John James, Peter Joyce, and Edward McLachlan.

Oxford University Press, Walton Street, Oxford OX2 6DP

Oxford   New York
Athens   Auckland   Bangkok   Bombay
Calcutta   Cape Town   Dar es Salaam   Delhi
Florence   Hong Kong   Istanbul   Karachi
Kuala Lumpur   Madras   Madrid   Melbourne
Mexico City   Nairobi   Paris   Singapore
Taipei   Tokyo   Toronto

and associated companies in
Berlin   Ibadan

Oxford is a trade mark of Oxford University Press

© Roderick Hunt 1983
First published 1983
Reprinted 1984, 1985, 1986, 1987, 1988, 1990, 1991 (twice), 1993, 1994, 1995
ISBN 0 19 918176 4

Printed in Great Britain by the
University Press, Cambridge